FRANZ LISZT   LISZT FERENC

LÉGENDES

FÜR KLAVIER – FOR PIANO SOLO

Herausgegeben von – Edited by

Imre SULYOK

Imre MEZŐ

NEUE, ERWEITERTE AUSGABE
NEW, ENLARGED EDITION

Revidiert von – Revised by
Adrienne KACZMARCZYK

EDITIO MUSICA BUDAPEST

Editio Musica Budapest Zeneműkiadó Kft.
1132 Budapest, Visegrádi utca 13. • Tel.: +36 1 236-1104
E-mail: emb@emb.hu • Internet: www.emb.hu

ABKÜRZUNGEN – ABBREVIATIONS

Br. = *Franz Liszts Briefe*, Bd. 1–8, hg. von La Mara (Leipzig: Breitkopf & Härtel, 1893–1905) — **BrE** = *Letters of Franz Liszt*, vols. 1–2, ed. by La Mara, trans. by Constance Bache (London: H. Grevell & Co., 1894) — **EBK** = Eckhardt Mária: *Liszt Ferenc hagyatéka / Franz Liszt's Estate*, I. Könyvek / Books (Budapest: Liszt Ferenc Zeneművészeti Főiskola, 1986) — **LHK2** = Legánÿ Dezső: *Liszt and His Country, 1874–1886*, transl. Elisabeth Smith-Csicsery-Rónay (Budapest: Occidental Press, 1992) — **L–K** = *Franz Liszts Klavierunterricht von 1884–1886, dargestellt an den Tagebuchaufzeichnungen von August Göllerich*, hg. von Wilhelm Jerger (Regensburg: Gustav Bosse Verlag, 1975) — **L–MSW** = *The Letters of Franz Liszt to Marie zu Sayn-Wittgenstein*, transl. and ed. Howard E. Hugo (Cambridge, MA: Harvard University Press, 1953) — **NG2** = *The New Grove Dictionary of Music and Musicians*, 2nd edition, ed. by Stanley Sadie (London: Macmillan Publishers Ltd., 2001) — **NG2** plus a number = numbering in Mária Eckhardt–Rena Mueller: 'Franz Liszt, Works', in NG2, vol. 14, pp. 785–872 — **NLA** = Franz Liszt: *Neue Ausgabe sämtlicher Werke* (Budapest: Editio Musica Budapest, 1970–) — **NLE** = Ferenc Liszt: *New Edition of the Complete Works* (Budapest: Editio Musica Budapest, 1970–) — **PLB** = Franz Liszt: *Briefe aus ungarischen Sammlungen 1835–1886*, gesammelt und erläutert von Margit Prahács (Budapest: Akadémiai / Kassel: Bärenreiter, 1966) — **R** = Dr. Felix Raabe: „Verzeichnis aller Werke Liszts nach Gruppen geordnet", in Peter Raabe: *Franz Liszt*, Bd. II: Liszts Schaffen, 2., ergänzte Ausgabe (Tutzing: Schneider, 1968), S. 241–377, Zusätze S. 7–40 — **SH** = Michael Short–Leslie Howard, *F. Liszt: List of Works*, comprehensively expanded from the Catalogue of Humphrey Searle as revised by Sharon Winklhofer, in *Quaderni dell'Istituto Liszt* 3 (Milano: Rugginenti, 2004) — **SW** = Humphrey Searle, rev. by Sharon Winklhofer: 'Franz Liszt, Works', in *The New Grove Early Romantic Masters*, vol. 1, *Chopin, Schumann, Liszt* (New York & London: Macmillan, 1985) — **SzLM** = Mária Eckhardt: *Liszt's Music Manuscripts in the National Széchényi Library* (Budapest: Akadémiai Kiadó, 1986) — **WL3** = Alan Walker: *Franz Liszt*, vol. 3, *The Final Years, 1861–1886* (Ithaca, NY: Cornell University Press, 1997).

INHALT – CONTENTS

ZUR AUSGABE

Die Veröffentlichung der Kompositionen, Schriften und der Korrespondenz von Franz Liszt (1811–1886) sowie die Einordnung seines schöpferischen Lebenswerkes im Rahmen eines Katalogs begann im 20. Jahrhundert und dauert auch heute noch an. Die Veröffentlichung der Gesamtausgabe des musikalischen Lebenswerkes eröffnete die von Großherzog Carl Alexander von Sachsen-Weimar-Eisenach gegründete und durch die Herzogin Marie von Hohenlohe unterstützte Franz Liszt-Stiftung im Jahre 1907. Hierbei handelt es sich um die so genannte alte Gesamtausgabe, deren bis 1936 entstandenen 33 Bände ein Drittel des Lebenswerkes beinhalten. Die Modernisierung und die Beendigung dieser Publikation sich zum Ziele setzend initiierte die Editio Musica Budapest (EMB) im Jahre 1970 eine wissenschaftlich fundierte, neue, kritische Ausgabe des musikalischen Lebenswerkes.

Die Neue Liszt-Ausgabe (NLA) ist nach Gattung und Besetzung in zehn Serien unterteilt. Serie I (Werke für Klavier zu zwei Händen) lag in einer gemeinsamen Ausgabe von EMB und Bärenreiter-Verlag, Kassel, bis 1985 vor. Ab 1986 setzte EMB die Herausgabe der NLA eigenständig fort, und vollendete Serie II (Freie Bearbeitungen und Transkriptionen für Klavier zu zwei Händen) bis 2005. Das Grundprinzip der Edition der Serien I und II bestand darin, in erster Linie die endgültigen Fassungen der Werke zu veröffentlichen; von Frühfassungen erschienen im Anhang nur jene, die von der endgültigen Fassung wesentlich abweichen. 2005 begann die Herausgabe einer Reihe von 15 Supplementbänden mit dem Ziel, Frühfassungen der Werke für Klavier zu zwei Händen zu veröffentlichen, die von der endgültigen Fassung in geringerem Maße abweichen. In erster Linie sind es jene, die von Liszt selbst publiziert wurden, aber auch solche, die in Manuskript geblieben sind. In Spezialfällen werden auch umfangreichere Fragmente in den Supplementbänden publiziert.

Die Einzelausgaben der Klavierwerke Liszts, die in der NLA schon publiziert wurden, bieten nicht nur authentische, wissenschaftlich fundierte Notentexte samt kritischen Berichten, sondern auch komplette Frühfassungen und informative Vorwörter, die die Entstehungsgeschichte der jeweiligen Werke darstellt.

*

Wir waren bei der Edition bestrebt, die Besonderheiten der Kompositions- und Notationsweise Liszts weitestgehend zu berücksichtigen. Dementsprechend werden die irregulären, vereinfacht notierten Abschnitte nur dann den Regeln der heutigen Notation entsprechend umgestaltet, wenn dadurch das Notenbild nicht unnötig belastet wird. Der Rhythmus wurde nicht in regelmäßige Form gebracht, wo der Zeitpunkt des Anschlags eines Tones ausschließlich durch die Stellung dieses Tones bestimmt ist. Die Inkonsequenzen bei den Vereinfachungen werden dagegen in jedem Fall behoben. Die so genannte orchestermäßige Schreibweise ist überall beibehalten; die Notenstiele werden an solchen Stellen nicht in die übliche Richtung gezogen. Pausenzeichen bei zwei oder mehreren Stimmen in der gleichen Hand werden nur dann nachträglich gesetzt, wenn das Fehlen des Zeichens den Einsatz und die rhythmische Position der darauf folgenden Note unsicher gemacht hätte. Die Größe der Notenköpfe – normal (groß), kleiner und sehr klein – folgt genau den Quellen. Die aus einer Note bestehenden Vorschläge verschiedener Werte sind einheitlich als Achtel mit durchgestrichenem Stiel geschrieben; ihre Legatobögen wurden stillschweigend ergänzt. Der Wert der kleineren Noten wird nur dann korrigiert, wenn diese einen wesentlichen Bestandteil des Rhythmus bilden. Den Mehrwert der einen Hand und die ersetzenden Fermaten der anderen Hand, die über dem leeren Liniensystem stehen, werden unverändert belassen, Pausenzeichen wurden von uns unter ihnen nicht ergänzt. Bei chromatischen Bewegungen werden die Versetzungszeichen innerhalb des gleichen Taktes der besseren Lesbarkeit wegen mehrmals ausgeschrieben. Bei *quasi cadenza, a capriccio, a piacere* und *rubato* werden weder die Werte berichtigt, noch werden eventuelle Taktwechsel angemerkt. Die mit ossia überschriebenen, für Klaviere mit kleinerem Tonumfang als sieben Oktaven komponierten Abschnitte sind nur in den „Critical Notes" mitgeteilt, da sie für die heutige Praxis nicht mehr von Belang sind. Die ursprüngliche Bogensetzung der Quellen wird beibehalten und die gleichzeitig für zwei Stimmen geltenden Legatobögen bleiben ebenfalls unverändert. Wo die Quellen keinen Pedalgebrauch verlangen, wird er in dieser Ausgabe auch nicht vorgeschlagen, da das Fehlen der Bezeichnungen der Pedalführung nicht mit *senza pedale* identisch ist: die Anweisung *armonioso* verlangt z. B. einen ausgesprochen häufigen Gebrauch des Pedals. Beim Ausschreiben der Aufhebung von *una corda* wurde nicht nur die Dynamik, sondern auch der Tonfarbenwechsel berücksichtigt. Die *due pedali (mettez les deux pédales)* Anweisung der Quellen wird durch *con ped., una corda* ersetzt und die Veränderung jedes Mal in den „Critical Notes" erwähnt. Die in der Mitte zwischen den zwei Systemen stehenden >-Zeichen werden in beiden Händen ausgeschrieben. Die gestrichelte Linie nach Tempobezeichnungen wie *riten., accel.,* usw. zeigt die Geltungsdauer der gegebenen Anweisung an; folglich ist am Ende der gestrichelten Linie *a tempo* nicht extra ausgeschrieben. In den Werken ist Liszts ursprünglicher Fingersatz überall angegeben. Er wird nur in Fällen ergänzt, wo die Quellen den Fingersatz bei identischen Musikabschnitten erst an einer späteren Stelle oder Stellen mitteilen. Liszts eigenartige, heutzutage ungebräuchliche Vortragszeichen werden beibehalten. Von diesen beziehen sich die großen Λ, und > (Akzent-) sowie die ⌢ (Fermaten-) Zeichen auf die von ihnen umfasste Notengruppe. Die Bedeutung der anderen Zeichen wird in den Fußnoten zum Fall erklärt. *NB* bezeichnet immer eine Fußnote oder Anweisung, die der Vorlage entnommen ist, wogegen die mit Sternchen bezeichneten Fußnoten von den Herausgebern stammen. Ausnahmsweise kann auch eine mit einem Sternchen versehene Fußnote aus dem Original stammen; auf diesen Umstand weist dann die Bemerkung „Originalfußnote" hin.

Die Ergänzungen der Herausgeber werden folgendermaßen gekennzeichnet:

Buchstaben (Wörter, dynamische Bezeichnungen und *tr*-Zeichen) durch Kursivschrift;

Triolen- und andere Zahlen durch eine kleinere Schriftgröße und durch Kursivierung;

Versetzungszeichen, Staccatopunkte und -keile, Pedalzeichen, Pedalsternchen, Tenuto- und Akzentzeichen, Fermaten und Ornamente durch einen sehr feinen kleineren Stich;

Crescendo- und Diminuendo-Zeichen, runde Klammern,

Triller-Wellenlinien, große Akzentzeichen und Fermaten durch dünne Linien;

Taktvorzeichen durch dünn gedruckte Zahlen zwischen den zwei Systemen;

Bögen durch Strichelung;

Taktstriche durch Punktierung.

Alle anderen Ergänzungen stehen in eckigen Klammern.

Um den praktischen Zielsetzungen der NLA zu entsprechen und bei der Lösung von Problemen des Vortrages der Werkes zu helfen, haben die Herausgeber auch Liszts mündliche Vortragsanweisungen mit aufgenommen, die August Göllerich über Liszts Klavierstudien in seinem Tagebuch aufzeichnete und die in Lina Ramanns *Liszt-Pädagogium* sowie in anderen zuverlässigen Aufzeichnungen erhalten geblieben sind.

Zur Erleichterung der Identifizierung der Werke ist auch ihre Nummer im Werkverzeichnis von Raabe, Searle–Winklhofer, Eckhardt–Mueller und Short–Howard angegeben.

VORWORT

LÉGENDES
No. 1 St. François d'Assise: La prédication aux oiseaux /
Die Vogelpredigt
No. 2 St. François de Paule marchant sur les flots /
Der heilige Franziskus von Paola auf den Wogen schreitend

Im August des Jahres 1861 nahm Liszt Abschied von Weimar, um – nachdem er seine „symphonische Aufgabe [...] zum grösseren Theil gelöst" hat – sich in Rom niederlassend nunmehr die oratorische [zu] erfüllen".[1] Von seinen beiden großangelegten oratorischen Werken hat er die 1857 begonnene *Legende der heiligen Elisabeth* in Rom vollendet, den Plan des *Christus* aus dem Jahr 1853 hingegen zwischen den Jahren 1866–72 vollständig ausgearbeitet. Im Laufe der Jahre 1862–66, zwischen den beiden Hauptwerken, hat er die Portraits zweier weiterer Heiligen komponiert: Die Orchesterfassung der instrumentalen *Legenden*, welche je eine Szene des Lebens von Franziskus von Assisi und Franziskus von Paola verewigt, hat er 1863,[2] deren Klavierfassung im Jahre 1865 oder – deren Vorwort nach – 1866 fertiggestellt.

Die Beschreibung der als Grundlage für die Legenden dienenden wundersamen Ereignisse – die Programme der Kompositionen – hat Liszt im jeweils dem Notentext vorangesetzten Vorwort in vollem Umfang mitgeteilt. Die Geschichte über die den Vögeln gerichteten Predigt von Franziskus von Assisi (1181/1182–1226) hat er aus *Fioretti di San Francesco* zitiert, aus der Anthologie, welche über das Leben und die Taten des Begründers des Franziskanerordens (Ordo Fratrum Minorum, 1209) im 14–15. Jahrhundert zusammengestellt wurde.[3] Unter denen, die dem Heiligen von Assisi folgten, war auch der heilige Franziskus von Paola (1416–1507), der zum Begründer des kleinsten Ordens (Ordo Minimorum, 1474) innerhalb des Franziskanerordens geworden ist. Seine Beschreibung des wundersamen Meeresganges, des Überganges an der Meeresenge von Messina zitiert Liszt aus der Biografie des Theologen Giuseppe Miscimarra[4] aus dem 19. Jahrhundert. Neben der Arbeit von Miscimarra erwähnt Liszt als Inspirationsquelle auch die Franziskus von Paola darstellende Zeichnung von Eduard Jakob von Steinle

---

Schnapp): Editio Musica Budapest, Z. 40051, 1984. In der Orchesterfassung ist die Reihenfolge der beiden *Legenden* vertauscht.

[1] Liszt schrieb an Brendel am 8. November 1862 aus Rom: „Ich bin fest entschlossen, längere Zeit hier ungestört, unaufhaltsam und consequent fortzuarbeiten. Nachdem ich die mir gestellte *symphonische* Aufgabe in Deutschland, so gut ich es vermochte, zum grösseren Theil gelöst habe, will ich nunmehr die *oratorische* (nebst einigen zu derselben in Bezug stehenden Werken) erfüllen. Die Legende der heiligen Elisabeth, welche seit ein paar Monaten gänzlich beendet ist, darf nicht isoliert bleiben [...]." Br. 2, Nr. 9, S. 28.

[2] R 440, SW/SH 354, NG2 G27; Erste Ausgabe (Hg.: Friedrich

[3] Das Werk war in Liszts Budapester Bibliothek sowohl in italienischer als auch französischer Sprache zu finden: *Fioretti di S. Francesco*, testi di lingua secondo la lezione addottata dal P. A. Cesari e con brevi note filologiche di P. Fraticelle (Firenze, 1854), sowie *Fioretti ou petites fleurs de Saint François d'Assise* (Paris/Tournai, 1860). Vgl. EBK, S. 166.

[4] G. Miscimarra: *Vita di S. Francesco de Paola, fondatore dell'ordine de minimi* (Napoli, 1856). Ein Exemplar des Buches wurde laut dem Eintrag auf der inneren Titelseite von P. Enrico Ferrari de Pendri am 22. Oktober 1863 an Liszt geschenkt. Vgl. EBK, S. 169.

(1810–1886), welche er von Carolyne von Sayn-Wittgenstein als Geschenk bekam und welches später auf seinen persönlichen Wunsch als Vorlage für das Titelbild der französischen Ausgabe des Werkes diente. Liszt erwähnt die Zeichnung Steinles im Zusammenhang mit dem von ihm als „Franciscus-Lied" bezeichneten Werk in zwei Briefen vom Herbst des Jahres 1860.[5] Es ist anzunehmen, dass das besagte Werk die erste Fassung der 1875 veröffentlichten Kantate *An den heiligen Franziskus* ist,[6] denn die in der dritten Strophe der Kantate auf den Text „O lasset uns bewahren heil'ger Liebe Gluten" gesungene Melodie ertönt auch in der Coda der 2. Legende (ab Takt 139).

In der Themenwahl Liszts haben allem Anschein nach auch persönliche Motivation eine Rolle gespielt. Es ist bekannt, dass sein Vater, Adam Liszt in seiner Jugend erwägte in den Franziskanerorden einzutreten, aber nach einem Jahr als Noviziat ihn seine Vorgesetzten von seinem Plan abrieten. Trotz dessen bewahrte er den Franziskanern eine gute Beziehung und auch als Schutzheiligen seines Sohnes wählte er einen Franziskaner, Franziskus von Paola. Der Komponist, den das Priestertum seit seiner Jugend anzog, hat die die niederen Orden der Priesterweihe am 30. Juli des Jahres 1865 in Rom empfangen. Zwei Wochen später, während der Vorbereitungen zur Erstaufführung der *Legende der heiligen Elisabeth* hat er sich im Zuge der Wiederbelebung seiner Beziehung zu den Franziskanern einen Franziskaner-Habit anfertigen lassen. Der Pressburger General des Ordens wurde benachrichtigt, Liszt hätte bei der Darbietung dieses Werkes am 15. August im Vigadó in dieser Kleidung dirigiert. Es ist fraglich, ob wirklich so geschah, denn die zeitgenössischen Fotografien, die Aufnahmen von Canzi und Heller zeigen ihn in Priestergewand.[7] Zum Werk passte der Franziskaner-Habit jedenfalls gut, da die heilige Elisabeth von Ungarn die Patronin des weltlichen Zweiges des Ordens ist. In Anbetracht all dessen kann es kein Zufall sein, dass Liszt die Uraufführung der Klavierfassung der durch die Taten der Heiligen aus Assisi und Paola inspirierten Legenden ebenfalls auf diese Zeit arrangiert hat: Er selbst trug beide ebenfalls im Vigadó am 29. August an einem Wohltätigkeitskonzert vor.[8]

In dem Jahr nach der Uraufführung sind die *Legenden* auch in Druck erschienen. Sie sind Cosima von Bülow, der jüngeren Tochter Liszts gewidmet, die zusammen mit ihrem Ehemann, Hans von Bülow bei der Uraufführung in Pest anwesend war. Die beiden *Legenden* wurden fast zeitgleich in 1866 in zwei Heften vom Verlag Rózsavölgyi & Társa und dem Pariser Heugel veröffentlicht. Die Ausgabe von Rózsa-

völgyi kann frühestens im Sommer erschienen sein, denn in seinem Brief vom 15. Juni bat Liszt Johann Nepomuk Dunkl, einen der Leiter des Verlages darum, die Veröffentlichung zu beschleunigen. Im gleichen Brief sprach er darüber, dass das Wandeln der Legende nach Paris ganz folgerichtig sei, wenn doch auch der heilige Franziskus selbst nach Paris kam.[9] Es ist jedoch fraglich ob Liszt dabei tatsächlich nur die zweite Legende meinte, oder eher zugunsten des Bonmots den heiligen Franziskus von Paola erwähnte, der von Ludwig XI gebeten und auf Wunsch von Papst Sixtus IV im Jahre 1483 tatsächlich nach Paris gereist war. Jedenfalls berichtete Liszt in seinem Brief vom 2. Oktober 1866 Franz Brendel bereits im Plural über die Neuerscheinung seiner *Legenden* bei Heugel.[10]

Von den handschriftlichen Quellen der beiden Kompositionen ist lediglich ein Bruchstück der 2. Legende erhalten geblieben. Das Notenblatt, welches die Takte 54–63 enthält, war einst im Besitz des Komponisten Mihály Mosonyi, kam dann in die Széchényi-Nationalbibliothek.[11] An demselben Ort wird das vollendete und ausgearbeitete Autograf der erleichterten Fassung (*version facilitée*) aufbewahrt.[12] Die in dieser Handschrift zu findenden, von fremder Hand stammenden Einträge – die Plattennummer und die Einteilung der Systeme – beweisen, dass Liszt diese Fassung bei Heugel zu veröffentlichen wünschte.[13] Hierzu kam es aber nicht, sodass die erleichterte Fassung erst 1975, in der Neuen Liszt-Ausgabe (Band I/10) veröffentlicht wurde.

Auch später trat Liszt mit den *Legenden* gern vor die Öffentlichkeit. Die Predigt von Franziskus von Assisi hat er bereits ein Jahr vor der Budapester Aufführung an einem Soirée von Pauline Viardot Garcia in Karlsruhe, im Rahmen des zwischen dem 21. und dem 26. August 1864 veranstalteten Festivals des Allgemeinen Deutschen Musikvereins gespielt.[14] Am 8. März 1866 trug er auf dem Empfang der Herzogin Metternich beide *Legenden* in der französischen Hauptstadt vor, wo er sich wegen des Einstudierens der *Graner Messe (Missa solennis)* zwischen dem 4. März und dem 22. Mai aufhielt.[15] Am 13. April berichtete er Carolyne von Sayn-Wittgenstein darüber, dass der namhafte französi-

---

5 Liszts Brief an Carolyne von Sayn-Wittgenstein vom 14. September, sowie 29. November 1860: Br. 5, Nr. 27, S. 61, sowie Nr. 43, S. 99.

6 R 494, SW/SH 28, NG2 J13; GA V/5.

7 WL3, S. 85–91.

8 *Zenészeti Lapok* [Musikalische Blätter] 5/47 (24. August 1865), S. 369.; 5/48 (31. August 1865), S. 377–378.

9 Liszt schrieb an Dunkl: „Nach seiner wunderbaren Schiffahrt über die Meerenge von Messina, kam ja der heilige Franciscus selbst nach Paris. Es ist also ganz folgerichtig, dass die Legende auch dorthin wandelt." PLB, Nr. 148, S. 126. Die Plattennummern des Ausgabe: N. G. 1229–1230. HM: 1866. febr. (S. 21.). Exemplare in der Széchényi–Nationalbibliothek, Signatur: *Mus. pr. 2430/I-II*.

10 Liszt schrieb an Brendel: „Bei Heugel in Paris (Director des *Ménestrel*) erscheint nächstens eine neue Auflage meiner Franziskus-Legenden." Br. 2, Nr. 47, S. 94. Die Plattennummern der Ausgabe: H. 4612. (1) und H. 4614. (2).

11 Signatur: *Ms. mus. 4.556*. Vgl. SzLM, Nr. 29, S. 106–107.

12 Signatur: *Ms. mus. 15*. Vgl. SzLM, Nr. 30, S. 107–108.

13 Plattennummer: H. 4629. Freundliche Mitteilung von François Heugel aus dem Jahre 1975.

14 WL3, S. 85. Über die beiden *Legenden* siehe weiter WL3, S. 56–59.

15 WL3, S. 98.

sche Maler und Illustrator, Gustave Doré (1832–1883) ihn mit seiner Zeichnung *Der heilige Franziskus auf den Wogen schreitend* beschenkt hat, welche durch die 2. Legende inspiriert worden war.[16] Das Bild – zusammen mit einer anderen Zeichnung Dorés, *Das Tor zur Hölle*, die durch den Eröffnungssatz der *Dante-Symphonie* inspiriert wurde – hing im Salon seiner Budapester Wohnung.[17] Am 20. März 1867 spielte er auf dem Wohltätigkeitskonzert[18] zugunsten der Opfer der Donauflut ebenfalls die 2. Legende.

Die beiden Klavierwerke erklangen des Öfteren auf den Meisterkursen Liszts,[19] wo er einige Takte der Stücke gelegentlich von dem Notentext abweichend spielte. Über den für die 1. Legende angefertigten, bisweilen verlorengegangenen neuen Schluss weiß man nur aus dem Tagebucheintrag seines späten Schülers, August Göllerich, vom 4. Juli 1884.[20] Die erweiterte Fassung des Schlusses der 2. Legende allerdings ist in einem Exemplar der Rózsavölgyi-Ausgabe erhalten geblieben, und zwar in Liszts eigenhändiger Niederschrift. Das Exemplar, das einige weitere Ergänzungen

und sogar Korrekturen von Liszt enthält, war im Besitz von Berthold Kellermann (1853–1926), der von 1873 bis 1878 Liszts Meisterkurse besuchte.[21] Dieser Fassung des Schlusses ähnelt die weitere Fassung (Takte 165–169), welche in der Aufzeichnung einer anderen Schüler Liszts, Ludovic Breitner (1855–um 1940) erhalten geblieben ist.[22] Auf der Rückseite des Notenpapiers notierte Breitner auch eine neue Fassung der Stimme der linken Hand in den Takten 103–110. Zwar kann die Handschrift Breitners philologisch nicht authentifiziert werden, dennoch lassen die stilistischen Merkmale, sowie die Ähnlichkeit zu der Fassung des Schlusses aus dem Jahre 1876 darauf schließen, dass diese Varianten wirklich von Liszt stammen können, weshalb der vorliegende Ausgabe alle drei Varianten enthält. Der Lehrer Breitners, Anton Rubinstein hat Franz Liszt im Jahr 1871 auf ihn aufmerksam gemacht,[23] sie haben einander aber erst Mitte März 1874 kennengelernt. Am 30. März spielte er jedenfalls Liszts Es-dur Klavierkonzert, in Anwesenheit des Meisters unter der Leitung von Hans Richter in Budapest.[24]

Februar 2019

Adrienne Kaczmarczyk
(Übersetzung von Dávid Spischák)

[16] Br. 6, Nr. 106, S. 110.
[17] Ihre Reproduktion ist auch heute noch im Franz Liszt Gedenkmuseum zu sehen. Die Originalzeichnungen werden im Museum der Schönen Künste in Budapest aufbewahrt, Signatur: *1905.1963.*
[18] WL3, S. 358–361.
[19] Vgl. L–K, S. 36, 54, 100, 107, 118, 121.
[20] Liszts Kommentar zum Stück: „Neuer Schluß!! Die Triller sehr lange und klingend. Die Recitative gut hervorheben." L–K, S. 54.
[21] Gegenwärtiger Eigentümer des Exemplars ist das Franz-Liszt-Museum in Bayreuth, Signatur: *A-M 5280/II.* Die erweiterte Fassung des Schlusses ist auf S. 37 der vorliegenden Ausgabe ediert; Liszts Korrekturen und Ergänzungen stehen in dieser Ausgabe in Klammer.
[22] Eine Kopie der Handschrift Breitners hat seine Schülerin Marguerite Sarasin-de Geymuller in ihrem Brief vom 28. April 1975 der NLA zur Herausgabe zugeschickt. Die Handschrift wird in der Musikabteilung der Zentralbibliothek in Zürich aufbewahrt: Nachlass von Marguerite de Geymuller, Signatur: *Varia D5.* Siehe S. 37 der vorliegenden Ausgabe.
[23] L–MSW, Nr. 78, S. 153.; PLB, Nr. 272, S. 166.
[24] LHK2, S. 15.

ABOUT THE EDITION

Publication of Ferenc Liszt's (1811–1886) musical works, writings and correspondence and the compilation of a thematic catalogue of his creative oeuvre began in the 20th century and is still in progress. The work of producing a complete edition of his musical œuvre was launched in 1907 by the Franz Liszt Stiftung established by Grand Duke Carl Alexander Saxe-Weimar-Eisenach and supported by Princess Marie von Hohenlohe. This so-called old Complete Edition, 33 volumes of which were completed by 1936, contains a third of Liszt's life-work. In 1970, with the aim of modernizing and completing this old edition, Editio Musica Budapest (EMB) launched a new, scholarly critical edition of the musical works.

The New Liszt Edition (NLE) comprises ten series, the works being grouped according to genre and scoring. Series I (Works for piano solo) was completed as a joint publication of EMB and Bärenreiter-Verlag, Kassel, by 1985. From 1986 on, EMB continued to publish NLE alone, completing Series II (Free arrangements and transcriptions for piano solo) by 2005. In publishing Series I and II priority was given to the definitive version of the works; of early versions only those were published in the appendix that differed significantly from the definitive form. In 2005 a series of 15 supplementary volumes was launched with the aim of publishing early versions of the solo piano works that differ less substantially from the definitive form: mainly those published by Liszt himself, but also some that remained in manuscript. In special cases more extensive fragments are also published in the supplementary volumes.

The separate editions of Liszt's solo piano works already published in NLE provide not only authentic texts based on scholarly research and critical notes but also complete early versions, as well as prefaces containing important background information.

*

In editing an attempt has been made to adhere to Liszt's compositional and notational peculiarities to the greatest extent possible. Thus the sections notated in an unusual, simplifying manner are not changed to agree with the rules of present-day notation if this makes the appearance of the score too crammed. The rhythm is not made regular in places where the time of striking a note is defined exclusively by the horizontal division. On the other hand, the inconsistencies within the simplifications are eliminated in every case. The so-called orchestral manner of notation is retained throughout: the stems are not drawn in the customary direction in these places. Rest signs for two or more parts in the same hand are only added if their absence would have made the timing, the place in the rhythm for sounding the subsequent note, uncertain. The size of the note heads – normal (big), smaller and very small – follows the sources exactly. Appoggiaturas of different value consisting of one note are written uniformly as quavers with a stroke through their stem and their slurs have been tacitly added. The value of very small notes is corrected only if they form an integral part of the rhythm. Fermatas substituted for additional value and placed above blank staves are left as they are, no rest sign being added under them. In chromatic passages the same accidentals are repeatedly written out within one and the same bar to improve legibility. In the case of *quasi cadenza, a capriccio, a piacere* and *rubato* directions the values are not modified, nor are any changes of time indicated separately. Sections marked *ossia* and written for pianos with a range of less than seven octaves are included in the 'Critical Notes' since their relevance for present-day practice is insignificant. The original slurring shown in the sources has been retained; even slurs referring simultaneously to two parts are left unchanged. Where the sources do not prescribe the use of the pedal no pedalling is suggested since the lack of pedal signs does not necessarily mean *senza pedale*: the *armonioso* style of playing, for example explicitly requires frequent use of the pedal. In cancelling *una corda* the requirements both of dynamics and of the change of timbre have been considered. The indication *due pedali* (*mettez les deux pédales*) in the sources is replaced by *con ped., una corda* in the present edition, the change of instruction being mentioned in the 'Critical Notes' in each case. The > signs occurring midway between two staves are written out in both hands. The broken line after *riten., accel.,* and other tempo indications marks the duration of validity of the given direction; consequently, *a tempo* is not added at the end of the lines. In the pieces Liszt's original fingering is given everywhere. Fingering is added in identical musical sections only if the sources indicate the fingering at a later place or places. Liszt's peculiar performance signs, which are no longer used today, have been retained. Of these the large Λ and > (accent) as well as the ⌒ (pause) signs affect the whole group of notes joined by them. The meaning of the other signs is explained in the footnotes on each occasion. *NB* always marks an original footnote or instruction; the footnotes supplied with an asterisk stem from the editors. In exceptional instances even a footnote with an asterisk may derive from the original. In this case, however, it is distinguished by the remark 'original footnote'.

Editorial additions are differentiated from the original as follows:
Letters (words, dynamics and trill signs) by italics;
Triplet etc. figures by small-sized numbers printed in italics;
Accidentals, staccato dots and wedges, pedal signs and asterisks, rest signs, tenuto and accent signs, fermatas and ornaments by smaller type;

Crescendo and diminuendo signs, round brackets, the wavy lines of trills, large-sized accent signs and fermatas by fainter lines;

Time signatures by fainter numbers between the staves;

Slurs by dotted lines.

All other additions appear between square brackets.

In order to meet the practical requirements of the NLE and to help solving the performing difficulties of the works involved, the editors have also included Liszt's verbal directions for performance put down by August Göllerich in his diary after his piano classes with Liszt as well as those preserved in Lina Ramann's *Liszt-Pädagogium* and in other reliable sources.

To facilitate identification of the works, their number in Raabe's, Searle–Winklhofer's, Eckhardt–Mueller's and Short–Howard's catalogues has also been added.

PREFACE

LÉGENDES

No. 1 St. François d'Assise: La prédication aux oiseaux / Die Vogelpredigt

No. 2 St. François de Paule marchant sur les flots / Der heilige Franziskus von Paola auf den Wogen schreitend

In August 1861 Liszt bade farewell to Weimar and went to settle in Rome, saying 'after having, so far as I could, solved the greater part of the *Symphonic* problem set me in Germany, I mean now to undertake the *Oratorio* problem'.[1] Of his two large-scale oratorios, *Die Legende der heiligen Elisabeth*, which he had begun in 1857, was finished in Rome, and *Christus,* which had been planned in 1853, was fully completed there in 1866–72. In the period 1862–66, between these two major works, he composed portraits of two more saints, namely the orchestral versions of the two *Legends* that evoke events from the lives of Saints Francis of Assisi and Francis of Paola respectively, both completed in 1863.[2] Their piano versions were composed in 1865 or – according to the date of their prefaces – 1866.

In these prefaces Liszt included a complete description of the programme of the two compositions, i.e. the miraculous events that inspired the legends. He quoted the story about Saint Francis of Assisi (1181/1182–1226) preaching to the birds from the *Fioretti di San Francesco*, an anthology compiled in the 14th and 15th centuries describing the life and deeds of the founder of the Franciscan order (Ordo Fratrum Minorum, 1209).[3] A follower of the saint of Assisi was Saint Francis of Paola (1416–1507), who was about to found the order of the smallest brothers (Ordo Minimorum, 1474). Liszt quotes the report about his miraculous walking on the waves across the Strait of Messina from a biography by the 19th-century theologian Giuseppe Miscimarra.[4] Besides this work the preface also cites as a source of inspiration a drawing of Saint Francis of Paola by Eduard Jakob von Steinle (1810–1886), which Liszt had received as a gift from Carolyne von Sayn-Wittgenstein; this later also served – at the composer's express wish – as a model for the title-page illustration of the work's French edition. Liszt also mentioned Steinle's drawing in connection with a piece he called 'Franciscus-Lied' in two letters written in the autumn of 1860.[5] The work in question was probably the first version of the cantata *An den heiligen Franziskus* published in 1875,[6] since the melody of the third strophe ('O lasset uns bewahren heil'ger Liebe Gluten') also appears in the coda of *Legend No. 2* (from bar 139).

Liszt's choice of topic was undoubtedly influenced by biographical factors. As is well known, as a young man his father Ádám Liszt had contemplated joining the Franciscan order, but after a year of the novitiate his superiors dissuaded him. He nevertheless remained on good terms with the order and chose a Franciscan saint – Saint Francis of Paola – as his son's patron saint. The composer, who had been attracted to the priesthood since his youth, took minor orders on 30 July 1865 in Rome. Two weeks later, while preparing for

---

[1] On 8 November 1862 Liszt wrote to Franz Brendel from Rome: 'Ich bin fest entschlossen, längere Zeit hier ungestört, unaufhaltsam und consequent fortzuarbeiten. Nachdem ich die mir gestellte *symphonische* Aufgabe in Deutschland, so gut ich es vermochte, zum grösseren Theil gelöst habe, will ich nunmehr die *oratorische* (nebst einigen zu derselben in Bezug stehenden Werken) erfüllen. Die Legende der heiligen Elisabeth, welche seit ein paar Monaten gänzlich beendet ist, darf nicht isoliert bleiben […].' Br. 2, no. 9, p. 28. English translation in BrE 2, no. 9, p. 33.

[2] R 440, SW/SH 354, NG2 G27; first edition (ed. Friedrich Schnapp): Editio Musica Budapest, Z. 40051, 1984. In the orchestral version the order of the two legends is reversed.

[3] This work was in Liszt's Budapest library in both Italian and French: *Fioretti di S. Francesco*, testi di lingua secondo la lezione addottata dal P. A. Cesari e con brevi note filologiche di P. Fraticelle (Firenze, 1854), and *Fioretti ou petites fleurs de Saint François d'Assise* (Paris/Tournai, 1860). Cf. EBK, p. 166.

[4] G. Miscimarra: *Vita di S. Francesco de Paola, fondatore dell'ordine de minimi* (Napoli, 1856). According to an annotation on the inner title page, a copy of this book was given to Liszt by P. Enrico Ferrari de Pendri on 22 October 1863. Cf. EBK, p. 169.

[5] Liszt's letters to Carolyne von Sayn-Wittgenstein dated 14 September and 29 November 1860: Br. 5, no. 27, p. 61, and no. 43, p. 99.

[6] R 494, SW/SH 28, NG2 J13; GA V/5.

the premiere of his *Die Legende der heiligen Elisabeth* in Pest and reviving his connections with the local Franciscans, he had a Franciscan habit made. The Pressburg general of the order was informed that Liszt had conducted in this vestment at the work's 15 August premiere at the Vigadó (Pest's Redoute). Whether this was true is open to question, since contemporary photographs prepared by Canzi and Heller show him in a cassock.[7] In any case, a Franciscan habit was well suited to the work, since Saint Elizabeth of Hungary is the patroness of the secular branch of the order. With all this in mind, it cannot be a coincidence that Liszt timed the first performances of the piano versions of his legends (which respectively drew their inspiration from the deeds of the two saints of Assisi and Paola) to the same period: he played both pieces on 29 August at a charity concert also held at the Vigadó in Pest.[8]

In the year following the premiere the *Legends* also appeared in print. They were dedicated to Cosima von Bülow, Liszt's younger daughter, who attended the Pest premiere together with her husband Hans von Bülow. The two legends were published in two volumes more or less simultaneously in 1866 by Rózsavölgyi és Társa in Pest and Heugel in Paris. The Rózsavölgyi edition could not have appeared before the summer, since in a letter dated 15 June of that year Liszt asked Johann Nepomuk Dunkl, one of the heads of the publishing house, to urge their publication. In the same letter he suggested that, 'after his miraculous voyage across the Strait of Messina, Saint Francis himself went to Paris. It is therefore fully consistent that the Legend should also wander there.'[9] It seems uncertain whether Liszt indeed had only *Legend No. 2* in mind, or was aiming at a *bon mot* by mentioning only Saint Francis of Paola, who indeed travelled to Paris in 1483 at the request of King Charles XI of France and Pope Sixtus IV. At any rate, in a letter written to Franz Brendel on 2 October 1866 Liszt already claimed in the plural that the new edition of his *Legends* was forthcoming from Heugel.[10]

The only manuscript source that has survived for either composition is a fragment of the autograph of *Legend No. 2*. The sheet that includes bars 54–63 of the piece was once owned by the composer Mihály Mosonyi, and later ac-

quired by the National Széchényi Library in Budapest.[11] The same institution holds the complete and fully worked-out autograph of the *version facilitée* of the same legend.[12] This manuscript includes annotations in a foreign hand – the plate number and the indication of line breaks – which leave no doubt that Liszt intended to have this version published by Heugel.[13] This plan, however, was not realized and so the facilitated version only appeared as late as 1975, in the New Liszt Edition (vol. I/10).

Liszt was happy to perform the *Legends* publicly also in later years. He played the Saint Francis of Assisi sermon a year before the Pest premiere at a soirée given by Pauline Viardot Garcia in Karlsruhe, the location of the festival of the Allgemeiner Deutscher Musikverein held from 21 to 26 August 1864.[14] On 8 March 1866 he performed both legends at a reception given by Princess Metternich in Paris, where he stayed from 4 March to 22 May to rehearse and perform his *Gran Mass* (*Missa solennis*).[15] On 13 April he informed Carolyne von Sayn-Wittgenstein from Paris that the famous French painter and illustrator Gustave Doré (1832–1883) had presented him with his drawing entitled *St Francis of Paola Walking on the Waters*, which was inspired by Liszt's *Legend No. 2*.[16] This image, together with *The Gate of Hell*, another drawing by Doré inspired by Liszt (the opening movement of the *Dante Symphony*), hung on the wall of the salon in Liszt's Budapest apartment.[17] On 20 March 1876 he again performed the *Legend No. 2* at a concert given in the Pest Vigadó for the benefit of the victims of the Danube flood.[18]

The two piano pieces were often played in Liszt's master classes,[19] where he occasionally played some bars different from the published version. The new conclusion written for *Legend No. 1* that August Göllerich mentioned in his diary on 4 July 1884 appears to be lost.[20] On the other hand, an expanded conclusion to *Legend No. 2* (bars 168–169) that Liszt prepared in 1876 has survived in the composer's own hand in a copy of the Rózsavölgyi edition. Liszt also entered some further additions and corrections into this copy that was owned by Berthold Kellermann (1853–1926), who at-

[7] WL3, pp. 85–91.

[8] *Zenészeti Lapok* [*Musical Papers*] 5/47 (24 August 1865), p. 369; 5/48 (31 August 1865), pp. 377–378.

[9] Liszt wrote to Dunkl as follows: 'Nach seiner wunderbaren Schiffahrt über die Meerenge von Messina, kam ja der heilige Franciscus selbst nach Paris. Es ist also ganz folgerichtig, dass die Legende auch dorthin wandelt.' PLB, no. 148, p. 126. Plate numbers of the edition: N. G. 1229–1230. HM: February 1866 (p. 21). Copies in National Széchényi Library, shelfmarks: *Mus. pr. 2430/I-II.*

[10] Liszt wrote to Brendel as follows: 'Bei Heugel in Paris (Director des *Ménestrel*) erscheint nächstens eine neue Auflage meiner Franziskus-Legenden.' Br. 2, no. 47, p. 94. Plate numbers of the edition: H. 4612. (1) and H. 4614. (2).

[11] Shelf mark: *Ms. mus. 4.556.* Cf. SzLM, no. 29, pp. 106 107.

[12] Shelf mark: *Ms. mus. 15.* Cf. SzLM, no. 30, pp. 107–108.

[13] Plate numbers: H. 4629. Kindly communicated by François Heugel in 1975.

[14] WL3, p. 72. On the two *Legends*, see also WL3, 56–59.

[15] WL3, p. 98.

[16] Br. 6, no. 106, p. 110.

[17] Reproductions of them are on display in the Liszt Ferenc Memorial Museum. The original drawings are kept in the Museum of Fine Arts in Budapest, accession number: *1905.1963.*

[18] WL3, pp. 358–361.

[19] Cf. L–K, pp. 36, 54, 100, 107, 118, 121.

[20] Liszt's commentary on the piece: 'Neuer Schluß!! Die Triller sehr lange und klingend. Die Recitative gut hervorheben.' L–K, p. 54.

tended Liszt's master classes from 1873 to 1878.[21] This alternative conclusion resembles another version (bars 165–169) that has come down to us as notated by another Liszt pupil, Ludovic Breitner (1855–c1940).[22] On the verso of the sheet Breitner also jotted down a new version of the left hand in bars 103–110. While the authenticity of Breitner's manuscript cannot be proven philologically, stylistic features and the similarity to the 1876 alternative conclusion suggest

that the versions stem from Liszt, therefore the present edition gives all three of them. Breitner was brought to Liszt's attention by his piano teacher Anton Rubinstein in 1871,[23] but his public debut was delayed until mid-March 1874. In any event, on 30 March he played Liszt's Piano Concerto in E-flat major in Budapest under the baton of Hans Richter in the presence of the composer.[24]

February 2019

Adrienne Kaczmarczyk
(Translated by Balázs Mikusi)

---

[21] This copy is kept in the Franz-Liszt-Museum in Bayreuth, shelfmark: *A-M 5280/II*. The expanded conclusion is printed on p. 37 of the present edition, while the corrections and additions are provided in the score in parentheses (cf. *Critical Notes*).

[22] On 28 April 1975 a copy of Breitner's manuscript was sent to NLE in a letter by his pupil Marguerite Sarasin-de Geymuller for publication. The original is kept in the Musikabteilung of the Zentralbibliothek in Zurich: Nachlass Marguerite de Geymuller, shelfmark: *Varia D5*. See p. 37 of the present edition.

[23] L–MSW, no. 78, p. 153; PLB, no. 272, p. 166.

[24] LHK2, p. 15.

À Madame la Baronne Cosima d Bülow (née Liszt)

LÉGENDES

R 17, SW/SH 175, NG2 A219

No. 1
ST. FRANÇOIS D'ASSISE
La prédication aux oiseaux – Die Vogelpredigt

FRANZ LISZT

Ce qu'on pourrait appeler le *motif spirituel* de la Composition suivante est tiré d'un des plus touchants épisodes de la vie de Saint François d'Assise, raconté avec une inimitable grâce de naïveté dans les *Fioretti di San Francesco,* petit livre devenu un des classiques de la langue italienne. Mon manque d'habileté, et peut-être aussi les bornes étroites de l'expression musicale dans une œuvre de petite dimension, appropriée à un instrument aussi dépourvu que le piano d'accents et de sonorités variées, m'ont obligé à me restreindre et à diminuer de beaucoup la merveilleuse surabondance du texte de la « prédication aux petits oiseaux. »

J'implore le « glorieux pauvret du Christ » (« Il glorioso poverello di Christo! ») de me pardonner de l'avoir ainsi appauvri.

Voici le texte de « *Fioretti* »:

…« E passando oltre con quello fervore, levò gli occhi, e vide alquanti albori allato alla via, in su'quali era quasi infinita moltitudine d'uccelli; dí che San Francesco si maravigliò; e disse a'compagni: Voi m'aspetterete qui nella via, e io andrò a predicare alle mie sirocchie uccelli, e entrò nel campo, e cominciò a predicare agli uccelli, ch'erano in terra; e subitamente quelli, ch'erano in sugli arbori, se ne vennero a lui, e insieme tutti quanti istettono fermi, mentre che San Francesco compiè di predicare; e poi anche non si partivano, insino a tanto ch'egli diè loro la benedizione sua, e secondo che recitò poi Frate Masseo a Frate Jacopo da Massa, andando San Francesco fra loro toccandoli colla cappa, nessun perciò si movea. La sostanza della predica di San Francesco fu questa: Sirocchie mie uccelli, voi siete molto tenute a Dio vostro Creatore, e sempre ed in ogni luogo il dovete laudare, imperocchè v'ha dato libertà di volare in ogni luogo, anche v'ha dato il vestimento duplicato e triplicato, appresso, perchè egli riserbò il seme di voi nell'arca di Noè, acciochè la spezie vostra non venisse meno, ancora gli siete tenuti per lo elemento dell'aria, che egli ha diputato a voi – oltre a questo, voi non seminate, e non mietete; e Iddio vi pasce e davvi li fiumi e le fonti per vostro bene; davvi i monti e le valli per vostro rifugio; e gli alberi alti per fare i vostri nidi; e conciossiachè voi non sappiate filare, nè cucire, Iddio vi veste, voi e vostri figliuoli: onde molto v'ama il vostro Creatore, poi ch'egli vi dà tanti benefici, e però guardatevi, sirocchie mie, dal peccato della ingratitudine, e sempre vi studiate di lodare Iddio. Dicendo loro San Francesco queste parole, tutti quanti quelli uccelli cominciarono ad aprire i becchi, e distendere i colli, e aprire l'ali e reverentemente inchinare i capi infino in terra, e con atti e con canti dimostrare, che'l Padre Santo dava a loro grandissimo diletto: e San Francesco con loro insieme si rallegrava e dilettava, e maravigliavasi molto di tanta moltitudine d'uccelli, e della loro bellissima varietà e della loro attenzione e familiarità; per la qual cosa egli in loro divotamente lodava il Creatore. Finalmente compiuta la predicazione, San Francesco fece loro il segno della croce;

e diè loro licenza di partirsi, e allora tutti quelli uccelli si levarono in aria con maravigliosi canti; e poi secondo la croce, ch'avea fatta loro San Francesco si divisono in quattro parti; e l'una parte volò inverso l'Oriente, e l'altra inverso l'Occidente, e l'altra inverso lo Meriggio, la quarta inverso l'Aquilone, e ciascuna schiera n'andava cantando maravigliosi canti; in questo significando che, come da San Francesco gonfaloniere della Croce di Cristo era stato a loro predicato e sopra loro fatto il segno della croce, secondo il quale eglino si divisono in quattro parti del mondo; così la predicazione della Croce di Cristo rinnovata per San Francesco si dovea per lui e per li frati portare per tutto il mondo; i quali frati, a modo che gli uccelli, non possedendo nessuna cosa propria in questo mondo, alla sola provvidenza di Dio commettono la lor vita. » (Capitolo 16. – Fioretti di San Francesco.)

Traduction

« Toujours sous la même inspiration, il leva les yeux et vit les arbres qui bordaient la route chargés d'une foule innombrable d'oiseaux, ce qui le surprit. Attendez-moi sur la route, dit-il à ses compagnons, pendant que j'irai prêcher à mes petits frères les oiseaux. Il entra dans le champ et s'adressa d'abord aux oiseaux qui étaient à terre; mais aussitôt ceux qui étaient perchés s'abattirent, et pas un ne bougea pendant tout le sermon; et ils attendirent la bénédiction du Saint pour s'envoler. Selon ce que raconte depuis frère Mattée a frère Jacques de Marra, saint François se promenait au milieu de ces oiseaux, les touchant de sa tunique sans qu'aucun d'eux se dérangeât. Le fond du sermon fut à peu près ceci:

‹ Mes bons petits oiseaux, vous êtes bien redevables à Dieu, votre créateur, que vous devez louer en tout temps et en tous lieux: il vous a permis de voler partout, vous a donné un double et triple vêtement; il a conservé dans l'arche de Noé votre espèce, afin qu'elle ne s'éteignit pas; vous lui devez l'élément de l'air qu'il vous a dévolu; voyez: vous ne semez pas, vous ne récoltez pas; cependant Dieu vous nourrit; il vous donne les rivières et les fontaines pour vous abreuver; il vous donne les monts et les vallées pour vous abriter, des arbres élevés pour faire vos nids; vous ne savez ni filer, ni coudre, et Dieu vous vêt, vous et vos petits. Il vous aime donc bien, votre Créateur, puisqu'il vous comble de tant de bienfaits. Gardez-vous du péché d'ingratitude, mes bons petits oiseaux; mettez tous vos soins à louer toujours Dieu. ›

Pepdant que le bon père parlait ainsi, les petits oiseaux ouvraient leur bec, déployaient leurs ailes, et courbaient la tête jusqu'à terre, faisant signe par leurs gestes et leur ramage que le sermon les comblait de joie. Saint François se réjouissait avec eux, s'étonnait du nombre, de la belle variété, de l'attention et de la familiarité de ces oiseaux, et louait en eux le Créateur.

Enfin, le sermon fini, il leur fit le signe de la croix et leur donna permission de partir. Alors tous ces oiseaux s'élevèrent dans les airs en faisant entendre des chants merveilleux, et selon la croix qu'avait faite saint François, se séparèrent en quatre bandes, dont l'une prit son vol vers l'orient, l'autre vers l'occident, la troisième vers le midi et la dernière vers le nord. Chaque bande remplissait les airs de ses chants, donnant à entendre par là que, comme saint François, ce gonfalonier de la croix du Christ, leur avait prêché

et fait le signe de la croix, selon lequel ils s'étaient dirigés vers les quatre parties du monde, ainsi la prédication de la croix du Christ devait s'étendre sur le monde entier, renouvelée par le Saint et ses frères qui, à l'instar des oiseaux, ne possédant rien ici-bas, confient leur vie à la Providence. »

(Chapitre 16. – « Petites fleurs de Saint François d'Assise. » – Paris 1860.)

Rome 1866

*) Die Sechzehntelpause gibt hier und bei Takt 8 nur an, dass die vorangehende Note „non ritardando", sehr kurz gespielt wird.

The semiquaver rest here and in bar 8 merely indicates that the note before it should be played 'non ritardando', very short.

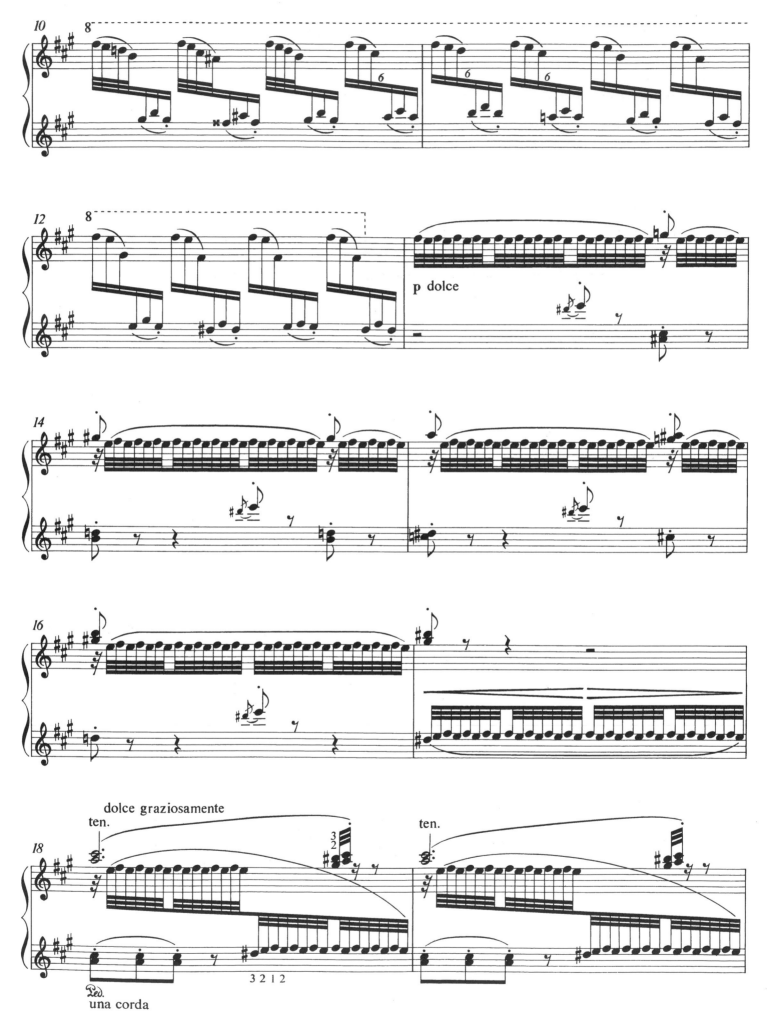

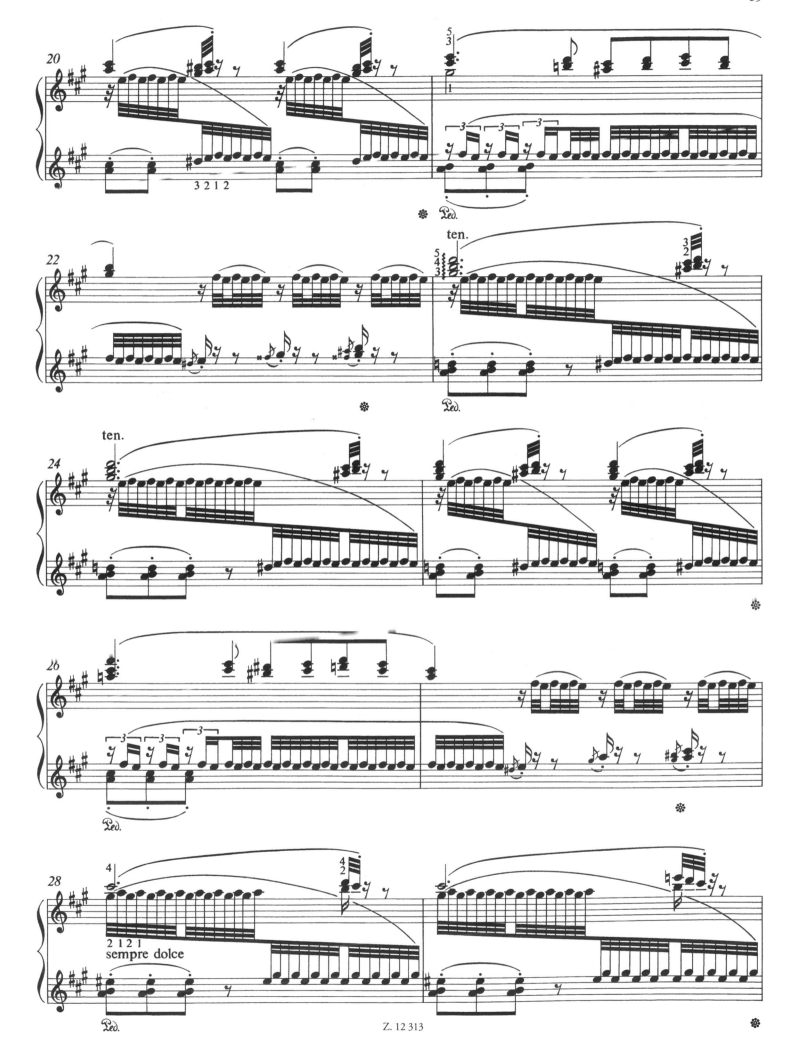

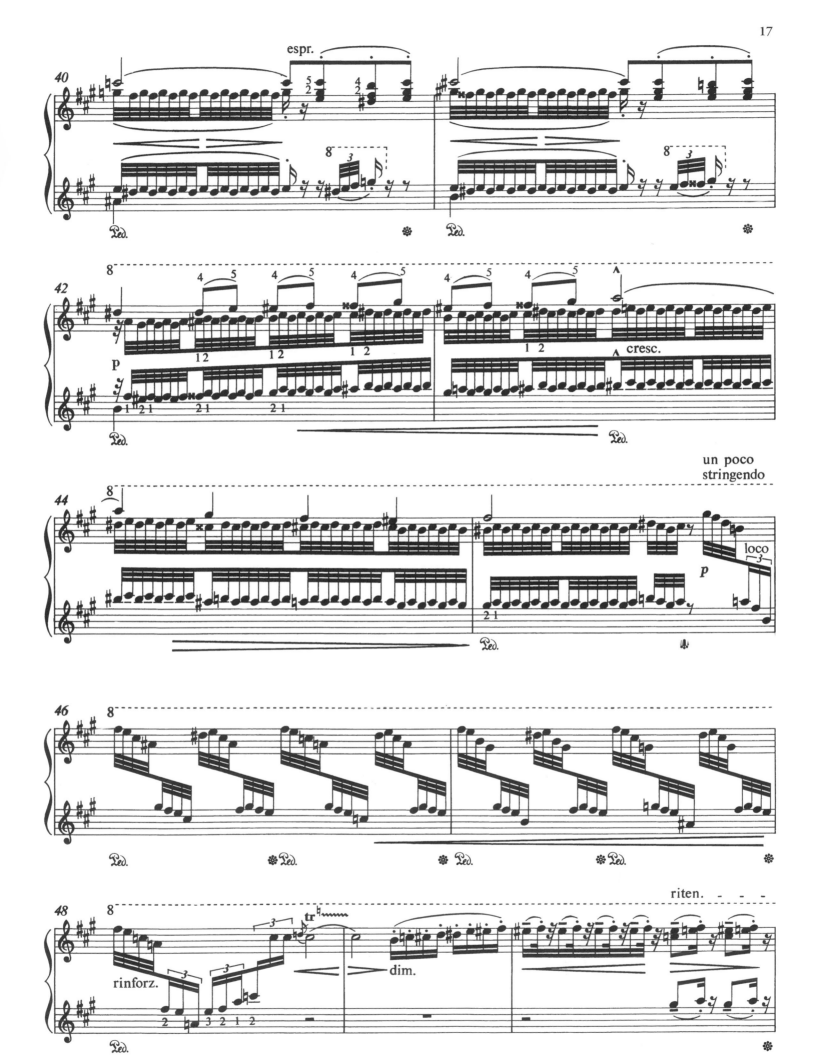

Recitativo
Un poco ritenuto il tempo

*) „Wo der Franciskus eintritt, das Recitativ ziemlich stark. …die 32tel rechts, die das Recitativ unterbrechen, immer sehr schnell." (L-K, 121)
'At the entry of Francis, the Recitativo fairly strong. …the right hand demisemiquavers which break up the recitative always very fast.' (L-K, 121)

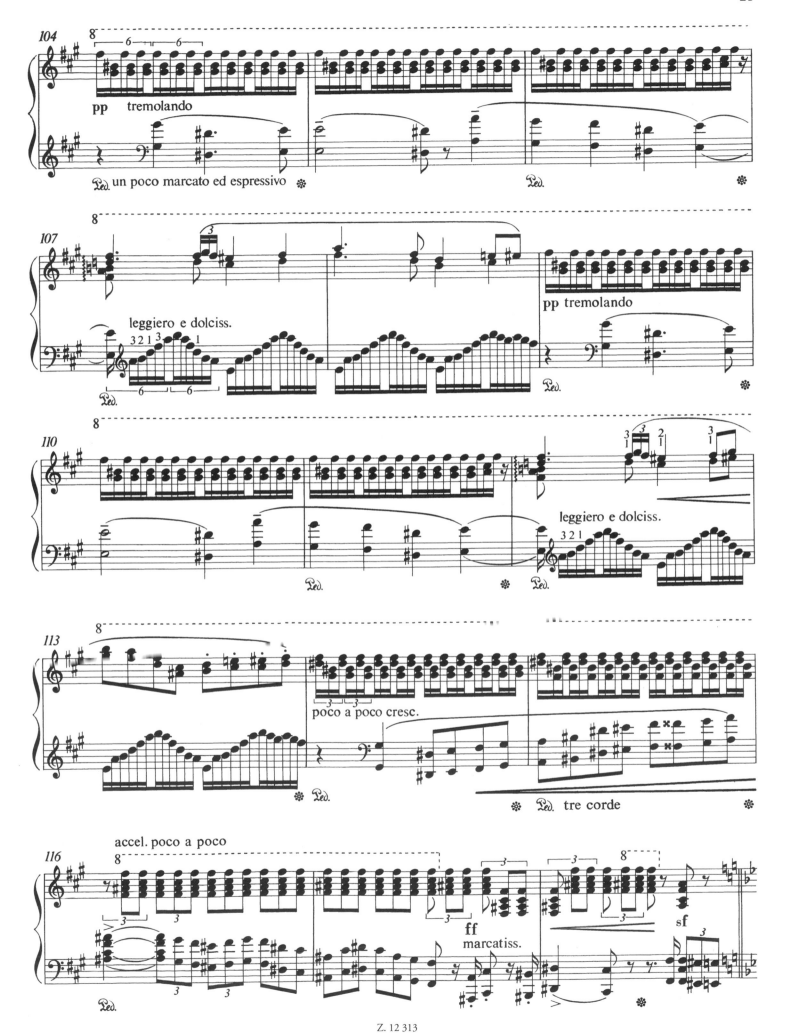

*) (L-K, 121)

No. 2

ST. FRANÇOIS DE PAULE MARCHANT SUR LES FLOTS

DER HEILIGE FRANZISKUS VON PAOLA
AUF DEN WOGEN SCHREITEND

Parmi les nombreux miracles de Saint François de Paule, la légende célèbre celui qu'il accomplit en traversant le détroit de Messine. Les bateliers refusèrent de charger leur barque d'un personnage de si peu d'apparence; il n'en eut garde, et marcha d'un pas assuré sur la mer.

Un des plus éminents peintres de l'école religieuse actuelle en Allemagne, M. Steinle, s'est inspiré de ce miracle, et dans un admirable dessin dont je dois la possession à la gracieuse bonté de Mme la Princesse Carolyne Wittgenstein, il a représenté, suivant la tradition de l'iconographie catholique:

Saint François debout sur les flots agités; ils le portent à son but, selon l'ordre de la Foi, qui maîtrise l'ordre de la Nature. Son manteau est étendu sous ses pieds; il lève une de ses mains comme pour commander aux éléments; de l'autre il tient un charbon ardent, symbole du feu intérieur qui embrase les disciples de Jésus-Christ; et son regard est tranquillement fixé au Ciel où reluit dans une gloire éternelle et immaculée la devise de Saint François, la parole suprème « Charitas! »

La Vie de Saint François de Paule, écrite en italien par Giuseppe Miscimarra, contient le récit suivant:

« Giunti in fine a vista del Faro di Messina e poi in quella parte del lido della Catona, trovò quivi una barca che portava in Sicilia doghe per botti. Presentatosi con i due compagni al padrone chiamato Pietro Coloso, dissegli ‹ per carità fratello portateci nell' isola su la vostra barca › e quelli ignorando la santità di chi lo pregava, gli chiese il nolo. E poichè rispos'egli di non averlo, quelli soggiunse di non aver barca per condurli. Presenti alla negativa quelli di Arena che aveano accompagnato il Santo, pregarono il padrone che imbarcasse que' poveri frati e di essere nella certezza che un di quelli era un santo. E s'è santo quegli, rispose con massima incivil- tà, che cammini su le acque e che faccia miracoli; e partito li lasciò sul lido. Senza turbarsi il Santo del tratto incivile di quel gonzo marinaro, perchè rincorato dal divino spirito che sempre lo assi- steva, si dissociò per poco da'compagni cd invocò con preghiere il divino aiuto in quel rincontro. Indi tornato a'compagni, disse loro, ‹ figliuoli allegramente; con la grazia di Dio abbiamo un naviglio migliore per passare › ma fra Giovanni innocente e semplice alcun legno non vedendo, con quale barca disse, Padre, noi passeremo, se quella è partita? Ci ha provvisti il Signore, egli rispose, di al- tro buon naviglio più sicuro su questo nostro mantello che stava per distendere sul mare. Sorrise fra Giovanni (perocchè il p. Paolo come prudente non aveva difficoltà del miracolo che il Santo gli significava) e con la sua solita semplicità disse, passiamo almeno sul mantello mio che ci sosterrà meglio perchè nuovo e non rattop- pato come il vostro. In fine disteso il mantello suo il nostro Santo su le acque, le benedisse in nome di Dio, e poi alzata una par- te del medesimo mantello, come vela bassa che veniva sostenuta dal suo bastone come albero, montò con i suoi compagni su quel prodigioso palischermo, e fece vela con istupore di quelli di Are- na, che guardando dal lido come velocemente percorreva le acque, gridavano piangendo e battevan le mani, come anco i marinari

del naviglio con l'ingrato padrone che chiedendogli perdono della negativa, lo invitava a salir sul legno: ma Dio che a glorificazione del suo santo nome voleva manifestare di aver sottoposto all'impe- ro del nostro Santo la terra e il fuoco non solo, ma anche le acque, gli fece disprezzare gl'inviti, e lo fece giugnere al porto prima del naviglio indicato. »…

« Gregorio XIII. avendo fatto dipingere nella sala del Vaticano quel miracolo, sembra che Dio abbia voluto che manifestazione continua la Chiesa con quella pittura ne fafacesse. » (Cap. 35. Vita di San Francesco di Paolo descritta da Giuseppe Miscimarra.)

« Arrivés en vue du phare de Messine, près de la plage de Cat- tona, saint François de Paule et ses deux compagnons virent là une barque prête à transporter en Sicile des douves de tonneaux. S'adressant au batelier, nommé Pierre Coloso, saint François lui dit: ‹ Pour l'amour de Dieu, prenez-nous sur votre barque et conduisez-nous à l'île. › Le batelier, ignorant la sainteté de celui qui lui parlait, demanda le prix du passage. Sur la réponse qu'il n'avait pas de quoi le payer, il lui signifia qu'il n'y aurait pas de barque pour le conduire. Témoins de ce refus, quelques habi- tants d'Arena qui avaient accompagné saint François de Paule prièrent le batelier d'embarquer ces pauvres moines, en assurant que l'un d'eux était un saint. ‹ Eh! si c'est un saint, répliqua du- rement Coloso, il n' a qu'à se promener sur les vagues et à faire un miracle! › Et il fit partir la barque en laissant les trois moines sur le rivage. Sans se troubler de ce mauvais procédé, saint Fran- çois, fortifié intérieurement de l'esprit divin qui l'assistait toujours, s'éloigna quelque peu de ses compagnons pour prier le Seigneur de le secourir en cette perplexité. Puis il revim à eux et leur dit: ‹ Or sus, allègres mes enfants! La grâce de Dieu nous a préparé un magnifique navire pour notre passage… avec ce manteau!… › et il l'étendit sur la mer. Fra Giovanni sourit naïvement et répli- qua: ‹ Prenons plutôt mon manteau, il nous soutiendra mieux, car il est neuf et non rapiécé comme le vôtre. › Quant à l'autre compagnon, fra Paolo, homme prudent, il crut de suite au miracle que le saint allait opérer. En effet, François de Paule, après avoir béni son manteau, l'élève en guise de voile, se soutient par son bâton qui sert de mât, se tient debout avec ses deux compagnons sur ce prodigieux esquif, et navigue de la sorte… Les habitants d'Arena sur le rivage, stupéfaits de la rapidité de ce trajet miracu- leux, crient, pleurent, battent des mains, comme aussi les bateliers de la barque de Coloso, et celui-ci même, qui demande pardon au saint et le supplie de monter sur sa barque. Mais le Seigneur voulut manifester que pour glorifier son saint nom avait soumis à notre Saint non-seulement la terre et le feu, mais encore la mer, lui ins- pira de ne tenir nul compte de l'offre du batelier, et le fit arriver au port bien avant la barque de Coloso. »

« Grégoire XIII a fait peindre dans la grande salle du Vatican ce miracle, que Dieu semble ainsi vouloir manifester perpétuelle- ment par son Église, avec cette peinture. » (Chapitre 35 de la vie de Saint François de Paule, par Giuseppe Miscimarra.)

Rome 1866

*) „Ziemlich stark anfangen … Erst von der 2. Zeile an das Thema **mf**. " (L-K. 118) / 'Begin fairly strongly … The theme **mf** only from the 2nd line.' (L-K, 118)

**) Das Marcato-Zeichen gibt hier, beim folgenden Takt und bei Takt 50 die Hervorhebung zweier Töne an. / The marcato sign here, in the following bar and in bar 50 indicates emphasis of two notes.

***) „Die Triole(n)… immer gut hervorheben gegen das Tremolo und ——— spielen." (L-K. 118) / 'The triplet(s)… to be well emphasized in contrast to the tremolo and played ——— .' (L-K. 118)

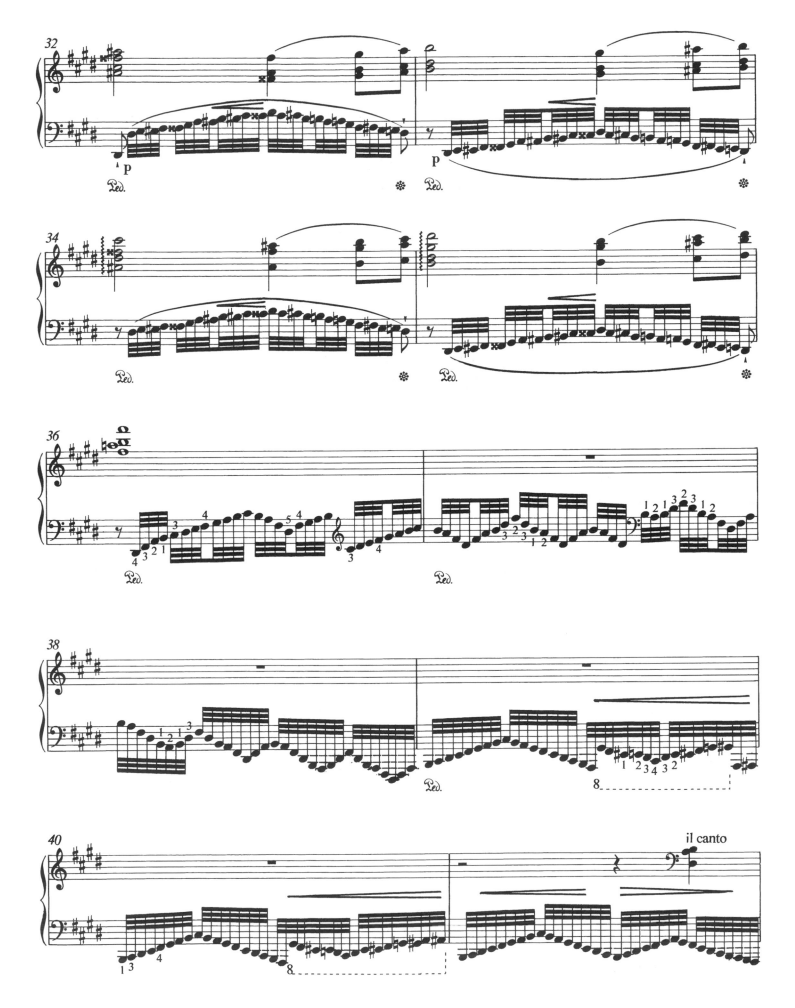

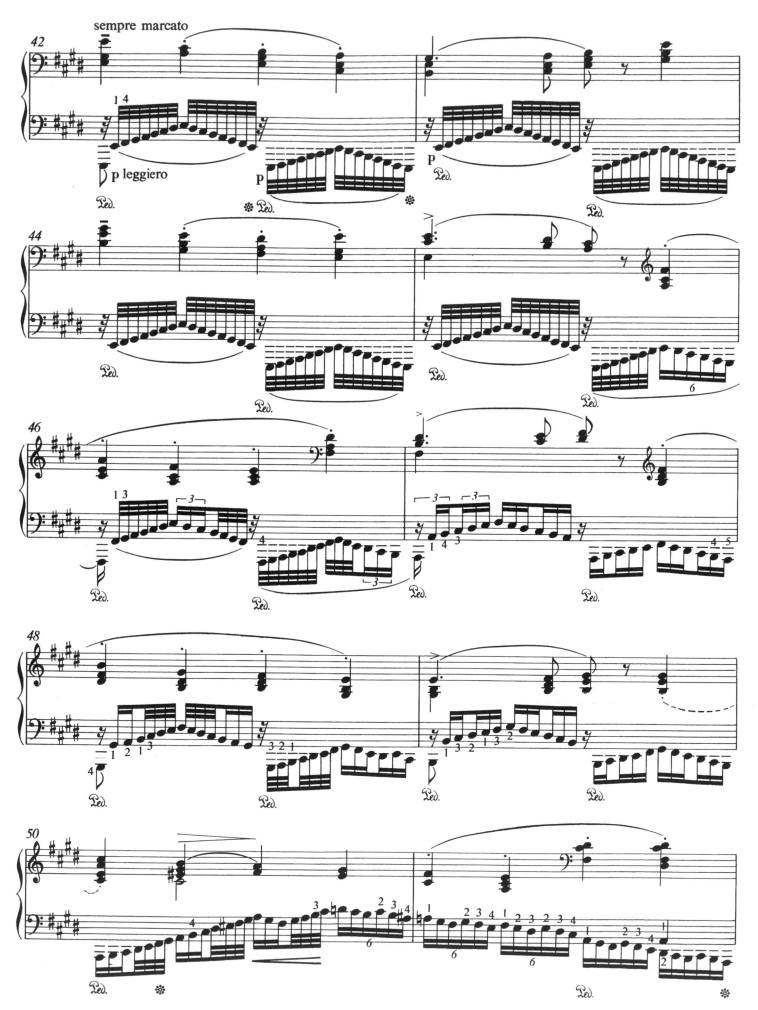

*) Die in Berthold Kellermanns Exemplar erhalten gebliebenen Korrekturen und Ergänzungen stehen in Klammern.
Corrections and additions found in Berthold Kellermann's copy are in parentheses.

*) Zu einer Alternativfassung der Takte 103–110 siehe S. 37. / For an alternative version of bars 103–110, see p. 37.

*) „.... die Cantilene ziemlich stark und sehr breit. Die Staccato-Akkorde der Begleitung nicht zu kurz abzupfen." (L-K, 119) / '... the cantilena fairly strong and very broad. The staccato chords of the accompaniment not clipped too short.' (L-K, 119)

*) Zu einer erweiterten Fassung der Takte 165–169 siehe S. 37. / For an extended version of bars 165–169, see p. 37.
**) Zu einer erweiterten Fassung der Takte 168–169 siehe S. 37. / For an extended version of bars 168–169, see p. 37.

LÉGENDE No. 2

Die Liszt zugeschriebene Alternativfassung der Takte 103–110, Kopie von Ludovic Breitner
Alternative version of bars 103–110, attributed to Liszt, Ludovic Breitner's copy

Zentralbibliothek, Zürich, Nachlass von Marguerite Sarasin-de Geymuller, Signatur: / Estate of Marguerite Sarasin-de Geymuller, shelfmark: *Varia D5.*

Die Liszt zugeschriebene erweiterte Fassung der Takte 165–169, Kopie von Ludovic Breitner
Extended version of bars 165–169, attributed to Liszt, Ludovic Breitner's copy

Zentralbibliothek, Zürich, Nachlass von Marguerite Sarasin-de Geymuller, Signatur: / Estate of Marguerite Sarasin-de Geymuller, shelfmark: *Varia D5.*

Erweiterte Fassung der Takte 168–169, Liszts eigenhändiger Eintrag von 1876 in der Erstausgabe (Budapest: Rózsavölgyi & Co.,
Plattennummer: N. G. 1230) / Extended version of bars 168–169, Liszt's autograph entry of 1876 in the first edition (Budapest:
Rózsavölgyi & Co., plate number: N. G. 1230)

Franz-Liszt-Museum, Bayreuth, Signatur / shelfmark: *A-M 5280/II.*

ANHANG – APPENDIX

No. 2

ST. FRANÇOIS DE PAULE MARCHANT SUR LES FLOTS

Version facilitée

R [17/2], SW [175/2], NG2 A219, SH 175/2bis

*) Das Marcato-Zeichen gibt hier und bei Takt 48 die Hervorhebung zweier Töne an. / The marcato sign here and in bar 48 indicates emphasis of two notes.

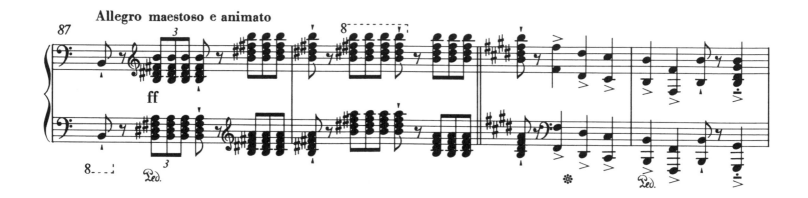

CRITICAL NOTES

LÉGENDES

Sources

A: The first edition of the pieces, which appeared in 1866: 'F. LISZT / LÉGENDES / POUR / PIANO / 1. ST. FRANÇOIS D'ASSISE / "La prédication aux oiseaux." / 2. ST. FRANÇOIS DE PAULE / marchant sur les flots. / PEST, chez RÓZSAVÖLGYI & Co.'
At the bottom of the title page: 'Exécuté par l'auteur au concert de Pest le 29 août 1865'. Plate No. N.G. 1229 and N.G. 1230. The dedication text takes up page [1], while Liszt's foreword and the quotations are on page [2].

B: Copies of the edition by Heugel, Paris, coming from Franz Liszt's estate, now held in the library of the Academy of Music in Budapest, ref. *12762–63*. They came out on 5 June, 1866, presumably at the same time as 'A' or shortly afterwards: 'A MADAME LA BARONNE COSIMA DE BÜLOW / (NÉE LISZT.) / Fr. Liszt / LÉGENDES / 1 Sᵗ FRANÇOIS / D' ASSISE / LA PRÉDICATION / AUX OISEAUX / 2 Sᵗ FRANÇOIS / DE PAULE / MARCHANT / SUR LES FLOTS'.
Obvious misprints and errors in these quotations have been tacitly corrected.

C: Copy of no. 2 of the Rózsavölgyi edition ('A') with autograph changes by Liszt, originating from Berthold Kellermann's estate, now kept in the Franz-Liszt-Museum in Bayreuth, shelfmark: *A-M 5280/II*. Liszt entered his changes in blue pencil and, in the case of the last two bars, in ink. He authorized his entries with dating and signature at the end of the piece: *1876 FLiszt*.
The changes entered by Liszt are:
73: **mp** (instead of **f**)
75: **mf** (instead of **f**)
91 and **119**: **p**
136–137: *8va bassa* under the left hand's staff
144: extension of the arpeggio sign upwards into the right hand's staff
169: insertion
170: marcato signs (instead of *fermate*)

No. 1 St. François d'Assise

The German subtitle appears, in brackets, in 'A' only.

4: the fingering has been added to agree with the identical part of **8**. The staccato dot on the last note has been added by analogy with the upbeat to **1**.

4 and **8**: the semiquaver rest in the right hand, although it represents excess time value in both sources, is not a misprint. These rests are rather a kind of performing instruction (see the footnote); their value merges with the fermata rests which follow them and for this reason the excess has not been marked by a change of time signature.

36: in the sources there is a staccato dot on the 2nd note in the upper part of the right hand. This has been omitted by analogy with **37, 40** and **41**.

45: the right hand ♮ has been added.

50: the extent of the *ritenuto* has been shown by a dotted line.

54 and **57**: the right hand slurs have been added by analogy with **60** and **63**.

58: the ✽ marking the release of the pedal has been added by analogy with **55, 61** and **64**.

79: in the sources the left hand slur begins at the 2nd note.

103: the ♮ before the 11th note in the left hand has been added.

No. 2 St. François de Paule marchant sur les flots

Supplementary source

D: The autograph manuscript held by the Music Division of the National Széchényi Library in Budapest under *Ms. mus. 4556*, which contains **54–63** of the piece. The German title appears, in brackets, in 'A' only.

42–49: in the sources the ✽ are given only in **47–49**, immediately before the next 𝕽𝖊𝖔. mark. Accordingly the ✽ have been added in **42** and they have been omitted in **47–49**.

47: the demisemiquaver rest is given erroneously in the sources as semiquaver rest.

49: the portato signs (slur and a staccato dot) on the 4th chord in the right hand and the 1st chord in the next bar have been added by analogy with **13–14**. (See also **47–48** of the simplified version.)

55: the fingering for the 10th and 14th notes in the left hand has been added by analogy with **61**.

57: in 'A' and 'B' the ⦥ lasts until the 8th note in the right hand and the ⦤ begins at the 11th note. Here the placing of the signs has been corrected to agree with 'D'.

61: in 'A' and 'B' the ⦥ lasts only to the end of the preceding bar, while the *rinforz.* starts at the beginning of the bar. Here 'D' has been followed by analogy with **55** .

63: the ⦥ and ⦤ have been added to agree with 'D' by analogy with **57**.

71: the right hand accent has been added by analogy with **65, 67** and **69**.

79: the accent and staccatissimo sign at the 2nd note in the left hand have been added to agree with the right hand.

87: in the sources there is no ♮ before the last note of the left hand.

88: the ⦥ have been added by analogy with **86, 87, 89** and **90**.

109 and **110**: the staccato dots on the 1st and 2nd notes in the lower part of the left hand have been added to agree with the analogous parts of **107** and **108**.

121: the left hand accents have been added to agree with the right hand, according to **113**, **115**, **117**, **118**, **123**, **125** and **126**.

159–160, **161**: in the sources the *crescendo* is between the two staves, in the middle, on both occasions. The position of these instructions has been corrected so that the first refers only to the left hand and the second only to the right hand.

No 2. St. François de Paule marchant sur les flots, Version facilitée

Source

The autograph manuscript held in the Music Division of the National Széchényi Library in Budapest, under *Ms. mus. 15*. The inscription, in the composer's handwriting, on the first page is: *F. Liszt / Légendes / No.2. St François d[e] Paule 'Marchant sur les flots' / (version facilitée)*. The manuscript consists of 8 pages of 20-stave music paper, measuring 31.5 × 24 cm. Liszt wrote the piece on pages 1–6 and he also numbered these pages. On page [7] there is in pencil the mark *H. 4629,* the plate number for a projected Heugel edition, and page [8] is empty. Tiny numbers concerning the distribution of the piece for engraving can be found on the music pages, which are written in ink.

Accidentals not given in the source have been added to this edition as follows:

♯: **15**, left hand, 4th note; **17**, left hand, 10th note; **25**, left hand, 14th note; **32** and **34**, left hand, 6th note; **36**, left hand, 6th, 12th and 16th notes; **37**, left hand, 8th note; **38**, left hand 2th and 16 th notes; **68**, right hand, 5th note; **69**, right hand, 6th and 7th notes; bar **77**, left hand last note *C♯*; **87**, right hand, 2nd note, *D♯* .

𝄪: **32–35**, left hand, 4th nore.

♭: **28**, left hand, 14th note; **29**, left hand, 6th note; **64**, right hand, 2nd and 9th notes; **65**, right hand, 6th note; **67**, right hand, 2nd and 6th notes.

♮: **20**, **21**, **23**, **28**, **31** and **114**, left hand, 2nd note; **22** and **30**, left hand, 6th note; **29**, left hand 2nd and 10th notes; **36**, left hand, 10th note; **37**, left hand, 4th, 10th and 14th notes; **38**, left hand, 4th, 8th and 12th notes; bar **100**, left hand, 1st note, both accidentals; **114**, right hand, 5th note; **120**, left hand, 2nd note, *d;* **120** and **121**, right hand, 2nd note; **122**, right hand, 10th and 11th notes, left hand, 9th note; **123**, right hand, 4th, 5th and last notes; **124**, all accidentals.

6: the left hand dynamic marking has been added to agree with the original version.

16, **18**: the fingering has been written in to agree with **20**.

22: the right hand accent has been added by analogy with **30**.

23: in the source there is no right hand slur or portato sign. They have been added here to agree with **25** and **27**, in accordance with the original version.

34: the 5th semiquaver in the left hand is an *A♯–C♯* third in the source. The *C♯* is obviously superfluous so it has been omitted.

35: the ✳ marking the release of the 🎵. has been added to agree with the three preceding bars.

37: the accidental originally written in (and necessary) before the 14th note of the left hand (and before the 2nd note of the following bar) has been deleted in the source.

40: in the source there is no tenuto sign on the first chord in the right hand. The sign has been added by analogy with **42** and to agree with the original version.

41: in the source there is a staccato dot at the 3rd chord in the right hand. This has been omitted here by analogy with **43**, **45** and **47**. In the source the 3rd and 4th slurs of the left hand do not appear. They have been added here by analogy with **40**.

In **42** and **43** the source gives the notes in the left hand only as repeat signs. Written out, they naturally require the slurs added in **41**, too.

50: in the source there is no left hand staccatissimo sign. Here it has been added by analogy with **51**, **56** and **57**.

51: the ✳ has been added to agree with **50** and the original version.

55, **61**: the 2nd, 3rd and 4th slurs in the right hand do not occur in the source. Here they have been added to agree with the preceding four crotchets.

56: there is no *p* in the source. Its necessity is proved by the *crescendo* which follows it and by the original version.

60: in the source the stem for the last quaver in the right hand is joined (in the opposite direction) to the *B* only, and does not go on to the *D*. Likewise the stem with the tail does not join the two notes in the 6th and 8th quavers of **61**, the 2nd, 6th and 8th of **62** and the 6th and 8th of **66**. The stems have been made consistent here and the stems with tails are joined to the lower notes at these points.

62: all the right hand slurs have been added by analogy with **54** and **61**.

65: in the source the last arpeggio sign in the left hand is missing, as are the arpeggio signs before all the chords in the following bar. The signs have been added here to agree with analogous **61–62**, **63–64** and **67–68** and the original version.

65–68: the 🎵. markings have been added by analogy with **63–64** and to agree with the original version.

71: the treble clef is missing in the source.

80: the staccatissimo sign for the 12th note in the left hand and the *ff* are both missing in the source.

82, **83**: in the source there are no staccatissimo signs for the first chord in either hand.

93: the ✳ has been added to agree with **91** and the original version.

112: in the source there are no staccatissimo signs for the 4th chord of the left hand and the 1st chord of the following bar.

144–147: the slurs in the left hand have been added by analogy with **142–143** and to agree with the original version.

157: the ⌢ signs have been added to agree with the original version.

Imre Sulyok, Imre Mező
(Translated by Fred Macnicol)

NEUE LISZT-AUSGABE
NEW LISZT EDITION

SERIE I / SERIES I
ORIGINALWERKE FÜR KLAVIER ZU 2 HÄNDEN
ORIGINAL WORKS FOR PIANO SOLO

Bd. / Vol.

SERIE II / SERIES II
FREIE BEARBEITUNGEN UND TRANSKRIPTIONEN FÜR KLAVIER ZU 2 HÄNDEN
(Die Komponisten der bearbeiteten Werke sind unter dem Titel des jeweiligen Bandes aufgezählt.)

FREE ARRANGEMENTS AND TRANSCRIPTIONS FOR PIANO SOLO
(The original composers of the arrangements are listed under the title of the volumes concerned.)

* A = Leinenband / Clothbound, B = Kartoniert / Paperback

10: Freie Bearbeitungen / Free Arrangements X – Z. A-B 12 399
   (Berlioz, Raff, Schubert, Wagner)
11: Freie Bearbeitungen / Free Arrangements XI – Z. A-B 12 400
   (Bach, Berlioz, Dietsch, Gounod, Meyerbeer, Schumann, Verdi, Wagner)
12: Freie Bearbeitungen / Free Arrangements XII – Z. A-B 12 401
   (Allegri, Bach, Beethoven, Gounod, Meyerbeer, Mozart, Wagner)
13: Freie Bearbeitungen / Free Arrangements XIII – Z. A-B 12 402
   (Bülow, Herbeck, Lassen, Mosonyi, Pezzini, Schumann, Spohr, Széchényi, Verdi,
   Wagner, Zamoyska)
14: Freie Bearbeitungen / Free Arrangements XIV – Z. A-B 12 403
   (Dargomijski, Händel, Huber, Knop, Lassen, Saint-Saëns, Szabadi–Massenet, Verdi, Zichy)
15: Freie Bearbeitungen / Free Arrangements XV – Z. A-B 12 404
   (Cui, Goldschmidt, Leßmann, Rubinstein, Schubert, Schumann, Tchaikovsky, Tirindelli,
   Verdi, Végh, Wagner)
16: Transkriptionen / Transcriptions I (Berlioz) – Z. A-B 13 353
17: Transkriptionen / Transcriptions II (Symphonies de Beethoven, Nos 1–4) – Z. A-B 13 354
18: Transkriptionen / Transcriptions III (Symphonies de Beethoven, Nos 5–7) – Z. A-B 13 355
19: Transkriptionen / Transcriptions IV (Symphonies de Beethoven, Nos 8–9) – Z. A-B 13 356
20: Transkriptionen / Transcriptions V (Schubert, Rossini) – Z. A-B 13 357
21: Transkriptionen / Transcriptions VI (Schubert: Schwanengesang; Winterreise) – Z. A-B 13 358
22: Transkriptionen / Transcriptions VII (Grand septuor de Beethoven, Op 20;
   6 Präludien und Fugen von Johann Sebastian Bach) – Z. A-B 13 359
23: Transkriptionen / Transcriptions VIII – Z. A-B 13 360
   (Beethoven, Hummel, Rossini, Wagner, Weber)
24: Transkriptionen / Transcriptions IX – Z. A-B 13 361
   (Bach, Beethoven, David, Lassen, Mozart, Cl. Schumann, R. Schumann, Wagner)

SUPPLEMENTBÄNDE ZU DEN SERIEN I–II
SUPPLEMENTARY VOLUMES TO SERIES I–II

1: Technische Studien / Technical Studies I – Z. A-B 12 266
2: Technische Studien / Technical Studies II – Z. A-B 12 267
3: Technische Studien / Technical Studies III – Z. A-B 12 268
4: Vingt-quatre grandes études und andere Werke / and other works – Z. A-B 14 499
5: Album d'un voyageur I, III; Clochette et Carnaval de Venise – Z. A-B 14 500
6: Harmonies poétiques et religieuses (Frühfassungen / Early versions) – Z. A-B 14 501
7: Magyar dallok / Ungarische Nationalmelodien – Z. A-B 14 502
8: Ungarische Rhapsodien / Magyar rapszódiák (Erstfassungen / 1st versions) – Z. A-B 14 503
9: Harold en Italie (Berlioz) und andere Werke / and other works – Z. A-B 14 504
10: Consolations und Erstfassungen anderer Werke / and 1st versions of other works – Z. A-B 14 505
11: Symphonies de L. van Beethoven Nos 5–7; Marche funèbre (N° 3, II)
   (Erstfassungen / 1st versions) – Z. A-B 14 506
12: Études d'exécution transcendante d'après Paganini
   Bravourstudien nach Paganinis Capricen und andere Werke
   (Erstfassungen / 1st versions) – Z. A-B 14 567
13: Années de pèlerinage II (Frühfassungen / Early versions) und andere Werke / and other works
   Z. A-B 14 711
14: Années de pèlerinage III, Weihnachtsbaum (Frühfassungen / Early versions) – Z. A-B 14 763
15: Klavierkonzert in A-Dur (Fassung für Klavier solo) und andere Werke /
   Piano Concerto in A Major (Version for Piano Solo) and other works – Z. A-B 14 764
*16: Lieder von Franz Schubert (Frühfassungen / Early versions) – Z. A-B 20 004

* In Vorbereitung / In preparation

WORKS BY LISZT FOR PIANO SOLO

The series of separate editions taken from the
New Liszt Edition is being revised*

♪ = Digital sheet music

* All volumes issued since 2014 contain prefaces in English and German, critical notes and early versions of the specific works. New volumes will also be published. Some older titles may be available as digital scores in the future. For up-to-date information please visit our website.